BAIZDON.com
London

The Smile Story

story - TEE DOBINSON

illustrations - ROBERT SHADBOLT

Two women worked at the Local Cafe.

One was always grumpy and never smiled at anyone. All her customers came out of the shop feeling bad tempered – and made grumpy faces all the way home.

In fact, she was known around town as the GRUMPY LADY.

The other woman in the cafe was always happy and smiled at everyone. All her customers came out smiling and soon passed their smiles onto other people. Of course, she was known as the HAPPY LADY.

Every day the Happy Lady gave out hundreds of smiles, and this is the story of just one of them.

7.00am

The Happy Lady smiled at her first customer, the road sweeper on his way to clean the streets.

The road sweeper was in a bad mood because he had to get up so very early, but as the smile passed to him he began to feel brighter. He started to sweep at super speed to make the streets clean and SPARKLING for everyone.

8.00am

The road sweeper smiled at a delivery driver as he raced by with all his parcels. The delivery driver was feeling cross because there was so much traffic, but as the smile passed to him he relaxed and turned up his music. He liked singing along – and so he did, very LOUDLY!

9.25am

The delivery driver smiled at a journalist who was cycling to her office.
The journalist was miserable thinking of all the bad news she had to write about, but as the smile passed to her she felt INSPIRED.

She had a GREAT IDEA – she would find some good news that would cheer everybody up and write about that instead.

10.45am

The journalist smiled at a taxi driver she saw at the traffic lights.
The taxi driver was down in the dumps as all of today's customers had been grumpy,
but as the smile passed to him he cheered up.

He thought about all the wonderful passengers he had met – including a famous football player who had given him a signed shirt. The taxi driver loved this shirt so much he wore it EVERY DAY!

11.30am

The taxi driver smiled
at his next customer,
a woman in a red dress.
The woman in the red dress was feeling
nervous – she was going to have a tooth
taken out! But as the SMILE passed to her
she began to calm down. The taxi driver
made her laugh with his funny stories and she
forgot all about her nerves.

TAXI

12.00pm

The woman in the red dress smiled at her dentist. The dentist was feeling stressed as he had so much to do today, but as the smile passed to him he took a deep breath and grinned (checking all his SPARKLY teeth in the mirror as he did). He felt sure he would get everything done in the end.

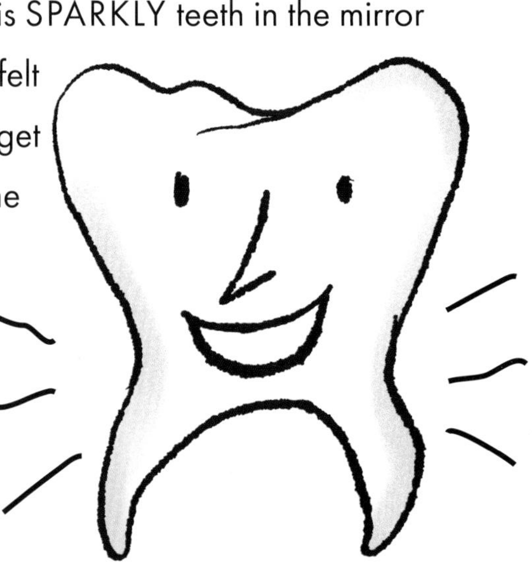

1.15pm

In his lunch break the dentist smiled at an old lady walking to the park.

The old lady was feeling a little bit lonely, but as the smile passed to her she began to feel much happier. She bent down and made a big fuss of her little dog, Buster. She told him he was the BEST DOG in the world – and he began to smile too!

2.30pm

The old lady smiled at a woman out in the park with her twins.

The woman with twins was fretting that her children were making too much noise, but as the smile passed to her she realised that they were happy squeals. So she bent down and joined in with the giggles of the twins. In fact, she was the NOISIEST one of all!

3.15pm

The woman with twins smiled at a lollipop lady.

The lollipop lady was feeling glum as her leg was aching, but as the smile passed to her she felt very LUCKY – she met so many friendly families. She spotted some children waving at her and, waving back, she went to help them cross the road. And do you know what? She forgot all about her aching leg!

4.45pm

The lollipop lady smiled at a school teacher. The school teacher was feeling sad because one of his pupils was in hospital, but as the smile passed to him he knew what to do.

He remembered the little boy loved storybooks, so he picked up one with very funny pictures that would make the boy LAUGH.

5.30pm

The school teacher smiled at the little boy in hospital.

The little boy was feeling fed up because he missed his friends, but as the smile passed to him he began to feel much jollier. He enjoyed looking at the pictures in the new book and, when his teacher read the story to him, he felt even BETTER!

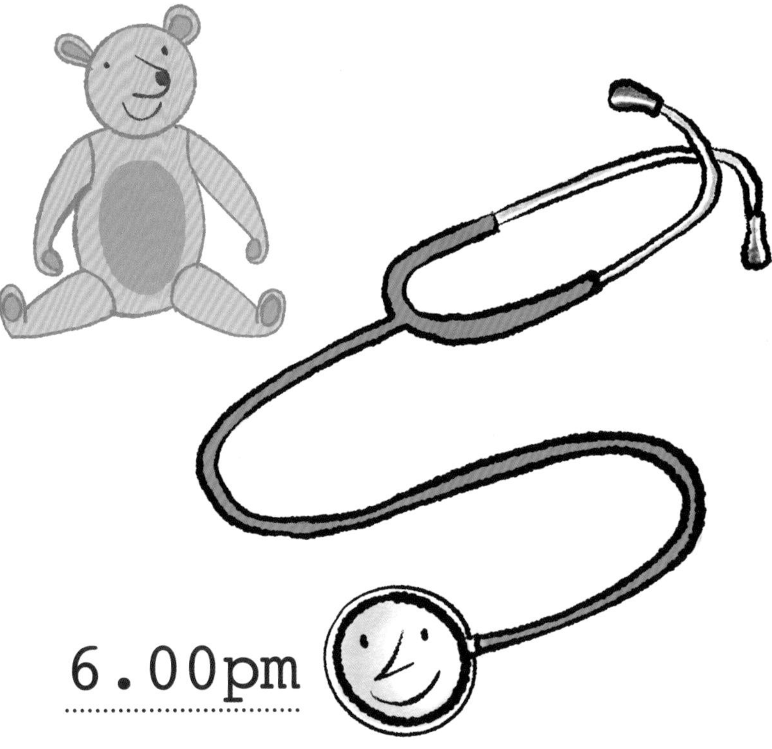

6.00pm

The little boy smiled at a nurse on the Children's Ward. The nurse was feeling very tired after a long day, but as the smile passed to her it gave her a BOOST. She decided to chat with every child on the ward before she went home.

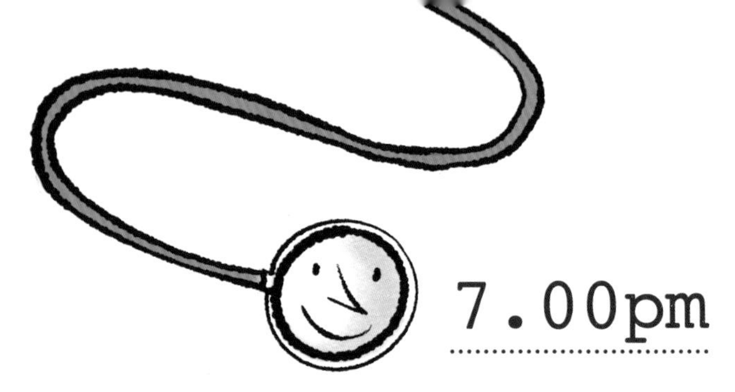

7.00pm

The nurse walked by the Local Cafe just as the two ladies were closing their shop. She smiled at the Happy Lady. The Happy Lady was pleased to get the smile back and of course, immediately gave the nurse a new smile in return.

7.01pm

The nurse was about to walk on when she noticed how very unhappy the Grumpy Lady looked. The nurse decided that, even though it wasn't easy, she would pass the new smile to the Grumpy Lady.

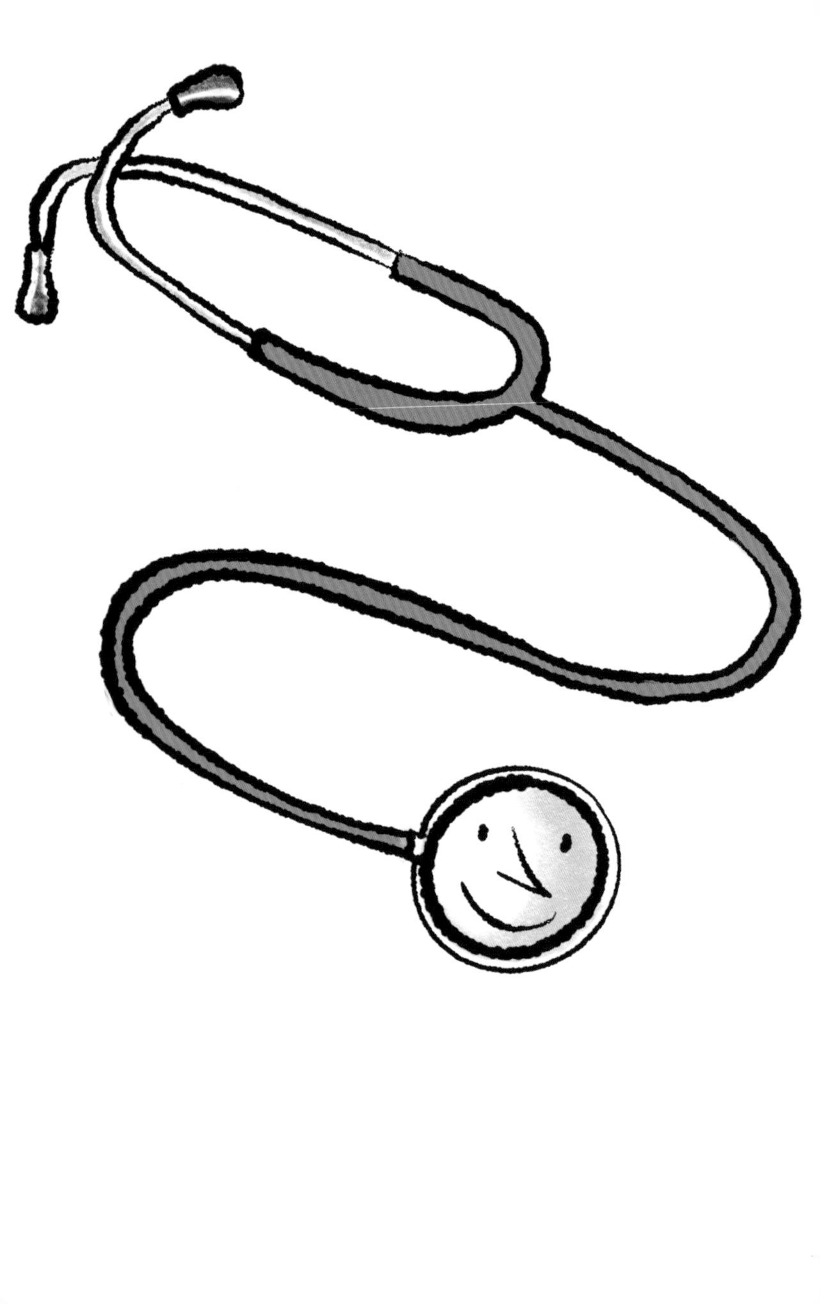

7.02pm

The Grumpy Lady was feeling grumpy as normal, but as the smile passed to her she felt something unusual happening. Her face began to change. Her cheeks twitched, her mouth moved and her lips began to curl upwards. SLOWLY, ever so slowly...

...SHE SMILED BACK!

Every day the Happy Lady begins hundreds of smile stories – see if you can start one today. Your smile will visit lots of people, and maybe it will come all the way back to you!

The END

(or maybe the beginning)

For Natasha, with love
&
for Phil, our friend (and sparkly dentist)

The Smile Story is published by
BAIZDON.com
19 Half Moon Lane, London, SE24 9JU

contact **team@baizdon.com**

Art direction and design Johnny Morris

A CIP catalogue copy of this book is available from the British Library.

ISBN: 978-1-9996022-7-7
eBook ISBN: 978-1-9996022-6-0

Anti-Inflammator and Dessert Cookbook

Stay healthy and Strengthen your immune system with these 50 recipes for your break moments

Natalie Worley

any techniques outlined in this book.

by reading this document, the reader agrees that under no circumstances is the author responsible for any losses, direct or indirect, which are incurred as a result of the use of information contained within this document, including, but not limited to, — errors, omissions, or inaccuracies.

Table of Contents

Crunchy and Salty Cucumber Salad

Prep Time: 10 Min | **Cook Time:** 0 Min | **Serve:** 4

- 2 candy-striped (Chioggiabeets, trimmed and peeled
- 2 Persian cucumbers, sliced thinly
- 1 medium radish, trimmed and sliced thinly Juice from 1 lemon
- ½ cup parmesan cheese, shredded A dash of flaky sea salt
- A dash of ground black pepper Olive oil for drizzling

1.Place all vegetables in a bowl.

2.Stir in the lemon juice and parmesan cheese. Season with salt and pepper to taste

3.Add olive oil or salad oil. Toss to mix everything.

Nutrition: Calories: 71; Fat: 4g; Carbs: 6g; Protein: 4g

Celery Salad

Prep Time: 5 Min | **Cook Time:** 0 Min | **Serve:** 4

- 3 cups celery, thinly sliced
- ½ cup parmigiana cheese, shaved 1/3 cup toasted walnuts
- 3 tablespoons extra virgin olive oil
- 1 tablespoon red wine vinegar Salt and pepper to taste

1.Place the celery, cheese, and walnuts in a bowl.

2.In a smaller bowl, combine the olive oil and vinegar. Season with salt and pepper to taste. Whisk to combine everything.

3.Drizzle over the celery, cheese, and walnuts. Toss to coat.

Nutrition: Calories: 142; Fat: 4g; Carbs: 13g; Protein: 4

Grilled Corn Salad with Feta Cheese

Prep Time: 5 Min | **Cook Time:** 15 Min | **Serve:** 6

- 6 large ears of corn, peeled and hulled
- ¼ cup chopped red onion ½ cup Feta cheese, crumbled
- 2 tablespoon extra-virgin olive oil Chopped mint for garnish
- Salt and pepper to taste

1.Heat the grill to medium high and grill the corn for 12 minutes. Cut the kernels off the cob and place on a bowl.

2.Add the rest of the ingredients and toss to mix everything.

Nutrition: Calories: 153; Fat: 8g; Carbs: 18g; Protein: 5g

Pear and Pomegranate Salsa

Prep Time: 10 Min | **Cook Time:** 0 Min | **Serve:** 3

- 2 fresh pears, cored and diced
- Seeds from 1 fresh pomegranate
- ½ onion, diced
- ½ cup fresh cilantro leaves, chopped Juice from ½ lime
- Salt and pepper to taste

1.Toss all ingredients in a bowl to combine. Serve immediately.

2.Best served with grilled meats.

Nutrition: Calories: 122; Fat: 1g; Carbs: 29g; Protein:2 g

Lentil Tomato Salad

Prep Time: 5 Min | **Cook Time:** 0 Min | **Serve:** 4

- 15 ounces canned lentils, rinsed and drained
- 1 ½ cups cherry tomatoes, sliced
- ¼ cup white wine vinegar 1/8 cup chives
- 1 tablespoon olive oil Salt and pepper to taste

1.Put all ingredients in a bowl. Toss to combine.

Nutrition: Calories: 231; Fat: 12g; Carbs: 23g; Protein:

10g

Asparagus Niçoise Salad

Prep Time: 20 Min | **Cook Time:** 20 Min | **Serve:** 4

- 1-pound small red potatoes, cleaned and halved
- 1-pound fresh asparagus, trimmed and halved
- 2 ½ ounces white tuna in water
- ½ cup pitted Greek olives, halved
- ½ cup zesty Italian salad dressing Water for boiling
- Salt and pepper to taste

1.Boil water in a stockpot over medium flame.

2.Put in the potatoes and cook for 20 minutes or the potatoes are tender. Blanch the asparagus for 3 minutes and set aside.

3.Place all ingredients in a bowl. Toss to mix all ingredients.

Nutrition: Calories: 223; Fat: 8g; Carbs: 23g; Protein: 16g

Bacon and Pea Salad

Prep Time: 10 Min | **Cook Time:** 5 Min | **Serve:** 6

- 4 bacon strips
- 4 cups fresh peas
- ½ cup shredded cheddar cheese ½ cup ranch salad dressing 1/3 cup chopped red onions Salt and pepper to taste

1.Heat skillet over medium flame and fry the bacon until crispy or until the fat has rendered. Transfer into a plate lined with paper towel and crumble.

2.In a bowl, combine the rest of the ingredients and toss to coat. Add in the bacon bits last.

Nutrition: Calories: 218; Fat: 14g; Carbs: 14g; Protein: 9g

Insalata Caprese

Prep Time: 10 Min | **Cook Time:** 0 Min | **Serve:** 8

- 2 ½ pounds tomatoes, cut into 1-inch pieces
- 8 ounces mozzarella cheese pearls
- ½ cup ripe olives, pitted
- ¼ cup fresh basil, sliced thinly Balsamic vinegar (optional Salt and pepper to taste
- 3 tablespoons olive oil

1.Place all ingredients in a bowl.

2.Season with salt and pepper to taste. Drizzle with balsamic vinegar if available. Toss to coat.

Nutrition: Calories: 160; Fat: 12g; Carbs: 7g; Protein: 6g

Salmon Salad with Walnuts

Prep Time: 10 Min | **Cook Time:** 10 Min | **Serve:** 2

- 2 salmon fillets
- 6 tablespoons balsamic vinaigrette, divided 1/8 teaspoon pepper
- 4 cups mixed salad greens 1/4 cup walnuts
- 2 tablespoons crumbled cheese Salt and pepper to taste

1.Brush the salmon with half of the balsamic vinaigrette and sprinkle with pepper.

2.Grill the salmon over medium heat for 5 minutes on each side.

3.Crumble the salmon and place in a mixing bowl. Add the rest of the ingredients and season with salt and pepper to taste.

Nutrition: Calories: 374; Fat: 25g; Carbs: 13g; Protein: 24g

Salmon White Bean Spinach Salad

Prep Time: 10 Min | **Cook Time:** 10 Min | **Serve:** 4

- 4 salmon fillets
- 15 ounces great northern beans, rinsed and drained ½ cup commercial vinaigrette of your choice
- 11 ounces baby spinach
- 1 red onion, cut into thin slices Salt and pepper to taste

1.Season the salmon fillets with salt and pepper. Place in a baking pan and bake for 4000F for 10 minutes or until the fish becomes flaky. Cool slightly. In a large bowl, toss the beans and vinaigrette. Toss in the spinach and onions. Divide the salad among four plates and top with salmon.

Nutrition: Calories: 577; Fat: 17; Carbs: 26; Protein: 76g

Balsamic Cucumber Salad

Prep Time: 10 Min | **Cook Time:** 0 Min | **Serve:** 6

- 1 large English cucumber, halved and sliced
- 2 cups grape tomatoes, halved
- 1 medium red onion, sliced thinly
- ½ cup balsamic vinaigrette ¾ cup feta cheese
- Salt and pepper to taste

1.Place all ingredients in a bowl.

2.Toss to coat everything with the dressing. Allow to chill before.

Nutrition: Calories: 90; Fat: 5g; Carbs: 9g; Protein: 4g

Sour Cream and Cucumbers

Prep Time: 15 Min | **Cook Time:** 0 Min | **Serve:** 8

- ½ cup sour cream
- 3 tablespoons white vinegar
- 1 tablespoon sugar
- 4 medium cucumbers, sliced thinly
- 1 small sweet onion, sliced thinly
- Salt and pepper to taste

1.In a bowl, whisk the sour cream, vinegar, and sugar. Season with salt and pepper to taste. Whisk until well-combined. Add in the cucumber and the rest of the ingredients. Toss to coat. Allow to chill before.

Nutrition: Calories: 62; Fat: 3g; Carbs: 7g; Protein: 2g

Minty Watermelon Cucumber Salad

Prep Time: 10 Min | **Cook Time:** 0 Min | **Serve:** 12

- 8 cups cubed seedless watermelon
- 2 English cucumbers, halved and sliced
- ¼ cup minced fresh mint
- ¼ cup balsamic vinegar
- ¼ cup olive oil
- Salt and pepper to taste

1.Place everything in a bowl and toss to coat everything.

2.Allow to chill before.

Nutrition: Calories: 60; Fat: 3g; Carbs: 9g; Protein: 1g

Easy Kale Salad

Prep Time: 10 Min | **Cook Time:** 0 Min | **Serve:** 8

- 10 cups kale, sliced thinly
- 1 apple, thinly sliced
- 3 tablespoons olive oil
- 2 tablespoons lemon juice
- ¼ cup crumbled feta cheese Salt and pepper to taste

1.Place kale in a bowl and massage kale until the leaves become soft and darkened. Add in the apples.
2.In another bowl, whisk the oil, lemon juice, salt, and pepper. Drizzle the sauce over the kale and sprinkle with cheese on top.

Nutrition: Calories: 113; Fat: 9g; Carbs: 6g; Protein: 4g

Pear Blue Cheese Salad

Prep Time: 10 Min | **Cook Time:** 0 Min | **Serve:** 10

- 12 cups romaine lettuce, torn
- 2/3 cup balsamic vinegar
- 2 medium pears, sliced
- 2/3 cup crumbled blue cheese
- 2/3 cup glazed pecans
- Salt and pepper to taste

1.Toss all ingredients in a bowl to combine.

2.Allow to chill before.

Nutrition: Calories: 133; Fat: 8g; Carbs: 12g; Protein: 3g

Salad Greens with Garlic Maple Salad

Prep Time:10 Min | **Cook Time:** 0 Min | **Serve:** 4

- 2 pounds mixed salad greens, washed
- 1/3 cup olive oil
- ¼ cup maple syrup
- 3 cloves of garlic, minced
- Juice from 1 lemon
- Salt and pepper to taste

1.Place the salad greens in a bowl.

2.In a smaller bowl, combine the olive oil, maple syrup, garlic, and lemon juice. Season with salt and pepper to taste.

3.Drizzle over the salad greens and toss.

Nutrition: Calories: 145; Fat:12 g; Carbs: 10g; Protein: 1g

Citrus Avocado Spinach Salad

Prep Time: 10 Min | **Cook Time:** 0 Min | **Serve:** 8

- 8 cups baby spinach; washed and drained
- 3 cups orange segments, seeded and halved
- 2 medium ripe avocadoes, peeled and sliced
- 1 cup blue cheese, crumbled
- Salad dressing of your choice
- Salt and pepper to taste

1.Place the spinach, oranges, and avocado slices in a bowl.

2.Add in the cheese and drizzle with the salad dressing of your choice. Toss to coat everything.

Nutrition: Calories: 168; Fat:10g; Carbs: 16g; Protein: 5g

Kale And Brussels Sprouts Salad

Prep Time: 10 Min | **Cook Time:** 0 Min | **Serve:** 6

- 1 small bunch kale, thinly sliced
- ½ pound fresh Brussels sprouts, thinly sliced
- ½ cup pistachios, chopped coarsely
- ½ cup honey mustard salad dressing
- ¼ cup parmesan cheese, shredded Salt and pepper to taste

1.Place all ingredients in a salad bowl. Toss to coat everything.

Nutrition: Calories: 207; Fat: 14g; Carbs: 16g; Protein: 7g

Pesto Tomato Cucumber Salad

Prep Time: 10 Min | **Cook Time:** 0 Min | **Serve:** 8

- ½ cup Italian salad dressing ¼ cup prepared pesto
- 3 large tomatoes, sliced
- 2 medium cucumbers, halved and sliced
- 1 small red onion, sliced Salt and pepper to taste

1.In a bowl, whisk the salad dressing and pesto. Season with salt and pepper to taste.

2.Toss gently to incorporate everything.

3.Refrigerate before.

Nutrition: Calories: 82; Fat: 5g; Carbs: 7g; Protein: 2g

Easy Asian Style Chicken Slaw

Prep Time: 10 Min | **Cook Time:** 0 Min | **Serve:** 8

- 3 ounces ramen noodles, cooked according to package
- 1 leftover rotisserie chicken, skin removed and shredded
- 16 ounces coleslaw mix
- 1 cup toasted sesame salad dressing
- 6 green onions, finely chopped
- Salt and pepper to taste

1.Place the noodles in a bowl and top with the chicken and coleslaw mix.

2.Drizzle with sesame salad dressing and season with salt and pepper to taste.

3.Mix and garnish with green onions last.

Nutrition: Calories: 267; Fat: 10g; Carbs: 18g; Protein: 26g

Cucumber and Red Onion Salad

Prep Time: 10 Min | **Cook Time:** 0 Min | **Serve:** 4

- 2 small English cucumbers, sliced thinly
- 1 cup red onion, sliced thinly
- 2 tablespoons white wine vinegar
- ½ teaspoon sugar
- ¼ teaspoon sesame oil Salt and pepper to taste

1.Put the cucumbers and red onions in a bowl.

2.In a small bowl, mix the white vinegar, sugar, and sesame oil. Season with salt and pepper to taste.

3.Pour over the cucumber and onions.

4.Toss to coat the ingredients.

Nutrition: Calories: 31; Fat: 1g; Carbs: 7g; Protein: 1g

Bacon Tomato Salad

Prep Time: 15 Min | **Cook Time:** 0 Min | **Serve:** 6

- 12 ounces iceberg lettuce blend
- 2 cups grape tomatoes, halved
- ¾ cup coleslaw salad dressing
- ¾ cup cheddar cheese, shredded
- 12 bacon strips, cooked and crumbled
- Salt and pepper to taste

1.Put the lettuce and tomatoes in a salad bowl.

2.Drizzle with the dressing and sprinkle with cheese.

Season with salt and pepper to taste then mix.

3.Garnish with bacon bits on top.

Nutrition: Calories: 268; Fat: 20g; Carbs: 11g; Protein: 10g

Easy Tea Cake

Prep Time: 10 min | **Cook Time:** 30 min | **Serve:** 12

- 6 tablespoons green tea powder
- 2 cups almond milk
- 4 eggs
- 2 teaspoons vanilla extract
- 3 ½ cups almond flour
- 1 teaspoon baking soda
- 3 teaspoons baking powder

1.In a bowl, mix the almond milk with green tea powder, eggs, vanilla, almond flour, baking soda and baking powder. Stir until smooth then pour into a cake pan and place in the oven to bake at 350 degrees F for 30 minutes. Slice and serve cold.

Nutrition: calories 170, fat 4, fiber 9, carbs 6, protein 5

581.

Coconut Cream

Prep Time: 2 hours | **Cook Time:** 5 min | **Serve:** 6

- 14 ounces almond milk
- 14 ounces coconut cream
- 1 teaspoon gelatin powder

1.In a pan, mix the almond milk with the cream and gelatin. Stir, bring to a simmer over medium heat and cook for 5 minutes. Divide into bowls and serve after 2 hours in the fridge.

Nutrition: calories 130, fat 4, fiber 3, carbs 7, protein 4 582.

Creamy Cantaloupe Salad

Prep Time: 5 min | **Cook Time:** 0 min | **Serve:** 1

- 1-ounce coconut cream
- 6 ounces cantaloupe, peeled and cubed
- A splash of lemon juice

1.In a bowl, mix the cantaloupe with the cream and lemon juice. Toss and serve.

Nutrition: calories 121, fat 6, fiber 2, carbs 15, protein 2

583.

Citrus cauliflower cake

Prep Time: 5 h and 30 m | **Cook Time:** 0 m | **Serve:** 10

For the Crust:

- cup dates, pitted 2½-cups pecan nuts
- Tbsps maple syrup or agave

For the Filling:

- ½-tsp lemon extract
- ½-tsp pure vanilla extract
- ¾-cup maple syrup or agave
- 1½-cups pineapple, crushed 1½-cups plain coconut yogurt 1-pc lemon, zest, and juice
- 1-tsp pure vanilla extract 3-cups cauliflower, riced

- 3-pcs avocados, halved and pitted 3-Tbsps maple syrup or agave
- A pinch of cinnamon

For the Crust:

1.Coat a baking tray using parchment paper. Set the outer ring of a 9- inch springform pan onto the baking tray.

2.Pulse the pecans in a food processor to a thoroughly ground texture. Put in the remaining crust ingredients, and pulse further until the mixture holds together.

3.Move and press the mixture to a uniform layer in the baking tray.

For the Filling:

1.Wipe the container of your food processor, and put in in the avocado, cauliflower, pineapple, syrup, and lemon zest and juice. Process the mixture to a smooth consistency.

2.Put in the cinnamon and the lemon and vanilla extracts. Pulse until meticulously blended. Pour the mixture over the crust. Put the tray in your freezer overnight, or for around five hours.

3.Take the cake out from your freezer, and allow it to sit at room temperature for about twenty minutes. Take away the outer ring.

4.For the Topping:

5.Mix in all the topping ingredients in a mixing container. Pour the mixture over the cake and spread uniformly.

Nutrition: || Calories: 667 || Fat: 22.2g || Protein: 33.3g || Sodium: 237mg || Total Carbohydrates: 88.1g || Fiber: 4.8g || Net Carbohydrates: 83.3g

Citrus strawberry granita

Prep Time: 15 min | **Cook Time:** 0 min | **Serve:** 4

- ¼ cup of raw honey
- ¼ lemon
- 1 grapefruit (peeled, seeded, and sectioned) 12 ounces of fresh strawberries, hulled
- 2 oranges (peeled, seeded and sectioned)

1.Put strawberries, grapefruit, oranges, and lemon in a juicer and extract juice according to the manufacturer's instructions.

2.Put 1½ cups of the veggie juice and honey to a pan and cook on moderate heat for five minutes while stirring constantly.

3.Remove it from heat and put in it to the rest of the juice.

4.Set aside for roughly thirty minutes.

5.Move the juice mixture into an 8x8-inch glass baking dish.

6.Freeze for 4 hours while scraping after every thirty minutes.

Nutrition: || Calories: 145 || Fat: 0.4g || Carbohydrates: 37.5g || Sugar: 32.4g || Protein: 1.7g || Sodium: 2mg

Coconut and chocolate cream

Prep Time: 2 h | **Cook Time:** 0 m | **Serve:** 4

- ½ teaspoon cinnamon powder
- 1cup dark chocolate, chopped and melted 1 teaspoon vanilla extract
- 2cups coconut milk
- 2 tablespoons ginger, grated
- 2 tablespoons honey

1.Throw all the ingredients into a blender and blend. Split into bowls and store in the refrigerator for about two hours before you serve.

Nutrition: || Calories: 200 || Fat: 3 || Fiber:5 || Carbohydrates: 12 || Protein: 7

Coconut butter fudge

Prep Time: 10 m | **Cook Time:** 0 m | **Serve:** 6

- ¼ teaspoon of salt
- 1 cup of coconut butter
- 1 teaspoon of pure vanilla extract 2 tablespoons of raw honey

1.Start by lining an 8 x 8 inch baking dish using parchment paper.

2.Melt the coconut butter, honey, and vanilla using low heat.

3.Place the mixture into the baking pan and place it in your fridge for about two hours before serving.

Nutrition: ǁ Total Carbohydrates: 6g ǁ Fiber: 0g ǁ Net Carbohydrates: ǁ Protein: 0g ǁ Total Fat: 36g ǁ Calories: 334

Coconut muffins

Prep Time: 5 m | **Cook Time:** 25 m | **Serve:** 8

- ¼ cup of cocoa powder
- ¼ teaspoon vanilla extract
- ½ cup ghee, melted
- 1 cup coconut, unsweetened and shredded 1 teaspoon baking powder
- 3 tablespoons swerve eggs, whisked

1.In a container, mix the ghee with the swerve, coconut, and the other ingredients, stir thoroughly and split it into a lined muffin pan.

2.Bake at 370 degrees F for about twenty-five minutes, cool down before you serve.

Nutrition: ǁ Calories: 324 ǁ Fat: 31g ǁ Carbohydrates: 8.3g ǁ Protein: 4g ǁ Sugar: 11g

Coffee Cream

Prep Time: 10 m | **Cook Time:** 15 m | **Serve:** 4

- ¼ cup brewed coffee
- 1 teaspoon vanilla extract 2 cups heavy cream
- 2 eggs
- 2 tablespoons ghee, melted 2 tablespoons swerve

1.In a container, mix the coffee with the cream and the other ingredients, whisk well and split it into 4 ramekins and whisk well.

2.Introduce the ramekins in your oven at 350 degrees F and bake for fifteen minutes.

Nutrition: Calories 300 || Fat: 11g || Carbohydrates: 3g || Protein: 4g || Sugar: 12g

Comforting Baked Rice Pudding

Prep Time: 10 m | **Cook Time:** 20 minutes **Serve:** 8

- ¼ cup of almond flakes
- ¼ cup of raw honey
- ½ tsp. of ground cardamom
- ½ tsp. of ground ginger 1 peeled and cut banana
- 1 tsp. fresh lemon zest, finely grated 1 tsp. of ground cinnamon
- 2 big organic eggs
- 2 cups of cooked brown rice
- 2 cups of unsweetened almond milk

1. Set the oven to 390 F, then grease a baking dish.

2. Spread cooked rice at the bottom of the readied baking dish uniformly.

3. In a big container, put together the coconut milk, eggs, honey, lemon zest, spices, and beat until well blended.

4. Put the egg mixture over the rice uniformly.

5. Position banana slices over egg mixture uniformly and drizzle with almonds.

6. Bake for approximately twenty minutes.

Nutrition: || Calories: 264 || Fat: 4.9g || Carbohydrates: 50g || Protein: 6.2g || Fiber: 2.9g

Cookie Dough Bites

Prep Time: 10 m | **Cook Time:** 5 m | **Serve:** 2

- ¼ cup Almond Flour
- ¼ cup Chocolate Chips, dairy-free & sugar-free
- ½ cup Almond Butter or any nut butter
- ½ tsp. Salt
- 1 ½ cups Chickpeas, cooked 1 tsp. Vanilla Extract
- 2 tbsp. Maple Syrup

1. First, place all the ingredients excluding the chocolate chips in a high-speed blender for about three minutes or until you get a thick, smooth mixture.
2. After this, move the mixture to a moderate-sized container.
3. Next, fold in the chocolate chips into the batter.

4. Check for sweetness and put in more maple syrup if required.

Nutrition: || Calories: 373 Kcal || Protein: 12.6g || Carbohydrates: 59.1g || Fat:10g

Creamy & Chilly Blueberry Bites

Prep Time: 2 h and 5 m | **Cook Time:** 0 m | **Serve:** 2

- 1-pint blueberries 2-tsp lemon juice
- 8-oz. vanilla yogurt

1.Coat the blueberries with the lemon juice and yogurt in a mixing container. Toss cautiously without squishing the berries.

2.Scoop out each of the coated berries and arrange them on a baking sheet coated with parchment paper. Place the sheet in your freezer for a couple of hours before you serve.

Nutrition: || Calories: 394 || Fat: 13.1g || Protein: 19.7g || Sodium: 164mg || Total Carbohydrates: 58.9g || Fiber: 9.7g || Net Carbohydrates: 49.2g

Creamy Frozen Yogurt

Prep Time: 10 m + 2-3 hours freezing | **Serve:**

Servings 3

- ½ cup of coconut yogurt
- ½ cup of unsweetened almond milk 1 tbsp. of raw honey
- 1 tsp. of fresh mint leaves
- 1 tsp. of organic vanilla extract
- 2 peeled, pitted and chopped medium avocados 2 tbsp. of fresh lemon juice

1. Throw all the ingredients into a blender apart from mint leaves and pulse till creamy and smooth.
2. Put into an airtight container then freeze for minimum 2-three hours.

3. Take off from the freezer and keep aside for about fifteen minutes.

4. With a spoon stir thoroughly.

5. Top with fresh mint leaves before you serve.

Nutrition: || Calories: 105 || Fat: 1.3g || Carbohydrates: 20.3g || Protein: 2.8 g || Fiber: 1.4g

Dark Chocolate Granola Bars

Prep Time: 10 m | **Cook Time:** 25 m | **Serve:** 12

- ¼ cup dark cocoa powder
- ¼ cup of flaxseed
- ½ cup dark chocolate chips 1 cup of walnuts
- 1 cup tart cherries, dried 1 teaspoon of salt
- 1 teaspoon of vanilla 2 cups buckwheat
- 2 eggs
- 2/3 cup honey

1.Preheat the oven to 350 degrees F.

2.Line with cooking spray your baking pan.

3.Pulse together the walnuts, wheat, tart cherries, salt, and flaxseed in a food processor. Everything must be chopped fine.

4.Mix the honey, eggs, vanilla, and cocoa powder in a container.

5.Put in the wheat mix to your container. Stir to blend well.

6.Include the chocolate chips. Stir once more.

7.Now pour this mixture into a baking dish.

8.Drizzle some chocolate chips and tart cherries.

9.Bake for about twenty-five minutes. Allow to cool before you serve.

Nutrition: Calories 364 || Carbohydrates: 37g || Cholesterol: 60mg || Fat: 20g || Protein: 6g || Sugar: 22g || Fiber: 4g || Sodium: 214mg

Date Dough & Walnut Wafer

Prep Time: 15 m | **Cook Time:** 18 m | **Serve:** 8

- ¼-cup coconut oil
- ¼-tsp sea salt
- ½-cup coconut, unsweetened
- ½-cup walnuts
- ½-tsp baking soda
- ½-tsp sea salt
- 1½-cup oats (divided)
- 18-pcs Medjool dates, pitted 1-pc egg
- 1-tsp lemon juice
- 2-Tbsps ground flaxseed
- 6-pcs Medjool dates, pitted and cut into four equivalent portions

1.Preheat the oven to 325°F. Coat a baking pan using parchment paper.

2.Pulse a cup of oats in a food processor until making a flour consistency.

3.Put in in the dates, coconut, baking soda, and sea salt. Pulse again until the dates completely break up.

4.Put in the remaining oats and walnuts, and pulse until the nuts break, but still a bit lumpy. Put in the flaxseed, egg, and oil. Pulse the mixture further until meticulously blended.

5.Set aside ½-cup of the date mixture to use as a topping later. Push down the rest of the mix to a uniform layer in the pan.

6.Wash your food processor, and put in all the date layer ingredients. Pulse the mixture until the dates completely break up and take on a light caramel color.

7.With wet hands, press the mixture down, smoothing it on the date mixture. Crumble and drizzle the reserved date mixture over the top.

8.Place the pan in your oven. Bake for eighteen minutes. Allow the wafer to cool to room temperature before cutting into 16 pieces.

Nutrition: || Calories: 203 || Fat: 6.7g || Protein: 10.1g || Sodium: 76mg || Total Carbohydrates: 28.3g || Fiber: 3g || Net Carbohydrates: 25.3g

Easy Peach Cobbler

Prep Time: 5 m | **Cook Time:** 20 m | **Serve:** 6

- ¼ brown rice flour
- ¼ cup coconut palm sugar, divided
- ¼ cup extra virgin olive oil
- ¼ cup ground flaxseeds
- ½ cup gluten-free oats
- ½ teaspoon cinnamon
- ¾ cup chopped pecans
- 5 organic peaches, pitted and chopped

1.Preheat your oven to 3500F.

2.Grease the bottom of 6 ramekins.

3.In a container, combine the peaches, ½ of the coconut sugar, cinnamon, and pecans.

4.Distribute the peach mixture into the ramekins.

5.In the same container, combine the oats, flaxseed, rice flour, and oil. Put in in the rest of the coconut sugar. Mix until a crumbly texture is formed.

6.Top the mixture over the peaches.

7.Put for about twenty minutes.

Nutrition: Calories 26 || Fat: 11g || Carbohydrates: 28g || Protein: 10g || Sugar: 12g || Fiber: 6g

Fall-Time Custard

Prep Time: 15 m | **Cook Time:** 60 m | **Serve:** 6

- ¼ tsp. of ground ginger
- 1 cup of canned pumpkin 1 cup of coconut milk
- 1 tsp. of ground cinnamon
- 1 tsp. of organic vanilla extract 2 organic eggs
- 2pinches of freshly grated nutmeg 8-10 drops of liquid stevia
- Pinch of salt

1.Preheat your oven to 350 degrees F.

2.In a big container, put together pumpkin and spices then mix.

3.In another container, put in the eggs and beat thoroughly.

4.Put in the rest of the ingredients then whisk till well blended.

5.Put in egg mixture into pumpkin mixture and mix till well blended.

6.Move the mixture toto 6 ramekins.

7.Position the ramekins in a baking dish,

8.Put in sufficient water in the baking dish about two-inch high around the ramekins.

9.Bake for approximately 1 hour or till a toothpick inserted in the middle comes out clean.

Nutrition: || Calories: 131 || Fat: 11.1g || Carbohydrates: 6.1g || Protein: 3.3g || Fiber: 2.3g

Fennel And Almond Bites

Prep Time: 10 m + 3 hours freezing time | **Cook Time:** 25 minutes | **Serve:** 10

- ¼ cup almond milk
- ¼ cup of cocoa powder
- ½ cup almond oil
- 1 teaspoon fennel seeds
- 1 teaspoon vanilla extract A pinch of sunflower seeds

1.Take a container and mix the almond oil and almond milk

2.Beat until the desired smoothness is achieved and shiny by using an electric beater. Stir in the remaining ingredients

3.Take a piping bag and pour into a parchment paper-lined baking sheet

4.Freeze for around three hours and stored in your refrigerator

Nutrition: || Total Carbohydrates: 1g || Fiber: 1g || Protein: 1g || Fat: 20g

Flourless Sweet Potato Brownies

Prep Time: 10 m | **Cook Time:** 30 m | **Serve:** 9

- ¼ cup Unsweetened Cocoa powder
- ½ cup Almond butter
- ½ cup Cooked sweet potato
- ½ tsp. Baking soda
- 1 big Whole egg
- 2 tsp. Vanilla extract
- 3 tbsp. Dairy-free chocolate chips, optional. 6 tbsp. Honey

1. Prep the oven by preheating to 350°F.

2. Coat a baking pan using parchment paper leaving a few extra inches on the sides to make it easier to discard or remove

3. Blend all the ingredients, excluding the chocolate chips until you get a super smooth and tender batter.

4. Move the creamy batter to your readied baking pan and use a spatula to spread it around, so it looks almost even.

5. Slide it in your oven, then bake for thirty minutes or until a knife inserted into the pan comes out clean.

6. Remove from the oven and leave to cool in the pan for fifteen minutes before putting it up on a wire rack.

7. If you decide to use the chocolate chip topping, put the chips in a microwave-safe dish and heat until it completely melts. Remove from the microwave and sprinkle over the brownies.

Nutrition: || Calories: 171 kcal || Protein: 5.17 g || Fat: 9.28 g || Carbohydrates: 20.01 g

Fried Pineapple Slice

Prep Time: 10 m | **Cook Time:** 8 m | **Serve:** 8

- ¼ cup of coconut oil
- ¼ cup of coconut palm sugar
- ¼ teaspoon of ground cinnamon
- 1 fresh pineapple (peeled and slice into big slices)

1.Warm a huge cast-iron frying pan on moderate heat.

2.Put in oil and sugar and cook until the coconut oil has melted while stirring constantly.

3.Put in the pineapple slices into two batches and cook for roughly 1- 2 minutes.

4.Flip the medial side and cook for approximately one minute. Carry on cooking for one more minute.

5.Repeat the steps with the rest of the slices.

6.Drizzle with cinnamon before you serve.

Nutrition: || Calories: 138 || Fat: 7g || Carbohydrates: 20.9g || Sugar: 15.7g || Protein: 0.6g || Sodium: 15mg

Fruit Cobbler

Prep Time: 10 m | **Cook Time:** 20 m | **Serve:**8

- ¼ Cup Coconut Oil, Melted
- ¼ Cup Coconut Sugar
- ½ Teaspoon Vanilla Extract, Pure
- ¾ Cup Almond Flour
- ¾ Cup Rolled Oats
- 1 Teaspoon Coconut Oil
- 1 Teaspoon Ground Cinnamon
- 2 Cups Nectarines, Fresh & Sliced 2 Cups Peaches, Fresh & Sliced
- 2 Tablespoons Lemon Juice, Fresh Dash Salt
- Filter Water for Mixing

1.Begin by heating the oven to 425.

2.Get out a cast-iron frying pan, coating it with a teaspoon of coconut oil.

3.Mix your lemon juice, peaches, and nectarines in the frying pan.

4.Prepare your food processor, mixing your almond flour, oats, coconut sugar, and remaining coconut oil. Put in in your cinnamon, vanilla, and salt, pulsing until the oat mixture looks like a dry dough.

5.If you need more moisture, put in filtered water a tablespoon at a time, and then break the dough into chunks, spreading it across the fruit.

6.Bake for 20 minutes before you serve warm.

Nutrition: || Protein: 4 Grams || Fat: 12 Grams || Carbohydrates: fifteen Grams

Fruit Salad

Prep Time: 10 m | **Cook Time:** 20 m | **Serve:** 2-3

- ½ of 1 Watermelon, chopped into little pieces
- 1 Pineapple, cut into little pieces 1 Pomegranate, small
- 1 Red Papaya, cut into little pieces 1 tsp. Ginger, freshly grated
- 4 Strawberries, chopped Dash of Turmeric

1. To start with, place all the fruits in a large-sized container.
2. Next, spoon in the turmeric and ginger over the fruits.
3. Toss thoroughly before you serve.

Nutrition: || Calories: 118Kcal || Protein: 1.6g || Carbohydrates: 36.6g || Fat: 0.5g

Glazed Banana

Prep Time: 10 m | **Cook Time:** 5 m | **Serve:** 2

- 1 peeled and cut under-ripened banana
- 1 tbsp. of filtered water 1 tbsp. of olive oil
- 1 tbsp. of raw honey
- 1/8 tsp. of ground cinnamon

1.In a nonstick frying pan, warm oil on moderate heat.

2.Put in banana slices and cook for approximately 1-2 minutes per side.

3.In the meantime, in a small container, put in water and honey and beat thoroughly.

4.Move the banana slices on a serving plate.

5.Instantly, pour honey mixture over banana slices.

6.Keep aside to cool to room temperature. Serve with the drizzling of cinnamon.

Nutrition: || Calories: 145 || Fat: 7.2g || Carbohydrates: 22.2g || Protein: 0.7g || Fiber: 1.6g

Glorious Blueberry Crumble

Prep Time: 10 m | **Cook Time:** 30 m | **Serve:** 6

- ½ cup of softened coconut oil
- ½ tsp. of ground cinnamon 1 cup of almond meal
- 1 cup of toasted and finely crushed almonds 2 tbsp. of coconut sugar
- 4 cups of fresh blueberries

1.Set the oven to 350F then lightly, grease a pie dish.

2.In a huge container, combine all ingredients apart from blueberries.

3.Split half of the almond mixture at the bottom of the prepared pie dish.

4.Put blueberries over almond mixture uniformly.

5.Top with the rest of the almond mixture uniformly.

6.Bake for minimum 30 minutes or till the top becomes golden brown.

Nutrition: || Calories: 411 || Fat: 34.3g || Carbohydrates: 24.9g || Protein: 7.4g || Fiber: 6.4g

Green Tea Pudding

Prep Time: 20 m | **Cook Time:** 10 | **Serve:** 3

- 1 Tsp. Matcha Green Tea Powder 1/4 Cup Brown Sugar
- 1/4 Cup Corn Starch
- 1/8-Tbsp. Cinnamon Powder 100g Butter
- 2 Cup Heavy Milk 3 Eggs
- Salt

1.In a big pot, mix brown sugar, milk, cornstarch, and matcha powder.

2.In moderate heat, keep whisking until combined.

3.Combine the hot batter with whisked eggs slowly.

4.Cook for three to five minutes.

5.Strain the mixture and put in butter.

6.Place the mixture in a container and place in your fridge for a few hours before serving.

Nutrition: || Calories: 359 kcal || Carbohydrates: 60 g || Fat: 3.0 g || Protein: 18.4 g

Grilled Peaches

Prep Time: 10 m | **Cook Time:** 10 m | **Serve:** 6

- ¼ cup of walnuts, chopped
- ½ cup of coconut cream
- 1 teaspoon of organic vanilla extract 3 medium peaches (halved and pitted) Ground cinnamon

1.Preheat the grill on moderate to low heat. Grease the grill grate.

2.Position the peach slices on the grill with the cut-side down.

3.Grill each side for three to five minutes or until the desired doneness is attained.

4.In the meantime, mix coconut cream with vanilla extract in a container. Beat until the desired smoothness is achieved.

5.Ladle the whipped cream over each peach half.

6.Top with walnuts and drizzle with cinnamon.

Nutrition: || Calories: 110 || Fat: 8g || Carbohydrates: 8.8g || Sugar: 7.8g || Protein: 2.4g || Sodium: 3mg

Hot Chocolate

Prep Time: 5 M | **Cook Time:** 5 M | **Serve:** 2

- ¼ tsp. Turmeric
- ½ tsp. Cinnamon
- 1tbsp. Coconut Oil 1 tbsp. Honey, raw 2 cups Almond Milk
- 2tbsp. Cocoa Powder, unsweetened

1.To start with, bring the almond milk to its boiling point in a deep deep cooking pan on moderate heat.

2.Now, bring this mixture to a simmer and then mix in the cocoa powder to it.

3.Next, spoon in the turmeric powder and cinnamon to it. Mix thoroughly/

4.Next, put in honey to it and once blended well, put in the coconut oil

5.Give the drink a good stir until everything comes together.

Nutrition: || Calories: 150 Kcal || Protein: 2.1g || Carbohydrates: 15.2g || Fat: 11.1gm

Lemon Sorbet

Prep Time: 10 m | **Cook Time:** 0 m | **Serve:** 2

- ½ cup of raw honey
- ½ cups of fresh lemon juice 2 cups of filtered water
- 2 tablespoons of fresh lemon zest, grated

1.Put into your freezer the ice-cream maker tub for a day before making the sorbet.

2.Combine all ingredients in a pan, excluding the freshly squeezed lemon juice and cook on moderate heat.

3.Simmer for minimum 1 minute, up to the sugar dissolves while stirring constantly.

4.Take away the mixture from the heat and put in lemon juice.

5.Move the combination to an airtight container and place in your fridge for around 2hours.

6.Put it into an ice-cream maker and process according to the manufacturer's instructions.

7.Put in one tablespoon of oil when the motor is running.

8.Return the ice-cream into the airtight container and freeze for roughly 2 hours.

Nutrition: || Calories: 305 || Fat: 1.5g || Carbohydrates: 74.9g || Sugar: 73.8g || Protein: 1.9g || Sodium: 40mg

Lightning Source UK Ltd.
Milton Keynes UK
UKHW020719270521
384465UK00005B/187